YO-CLG-562

. PETER *and* .
the FROG'S EYE

PETER *and the* FROG'S EYE

by

Julius King

with Photographs by LYNWOOD CHACE

THE JUNIOR LITERARY GUILD and
GROSSET & DUNLAP · *Publishers* · NEW YORK

Copyright, 1936, by GROSSET & DUNLAP, Inc.
Printed in U. S. A.

Peter and the Frog's Eye

IF PETER hadn't always been in such a hurry he would have seen a great many interesting things before that Saturday afternoon. But you see, he almost never walked; he always ran.

Zip — that was Peter going by! Whoosh — that was Peter on the way to Bob's house! Whizz — that was Peter coming home from school. No one could go faster, and of course, it *is* fun to go fast. But you have to watch the road when you're zooming along. And then you don't really see anything but your feet. You miss so much that way.

One Saturday afternoon right after lunch — a Saturday Peter will never forget — Peter had dashed to the meadow to go swimming with Bob. As always, he was first at the meeting place. Bob was nowhere in sight, so he sat down on a rock to wait.

The grass moved near his feet, and

Peter leaned down to look closer. There between two clumps of coarse grass two shiny eyes looked up at him. Like a flash his hand pounced down and caught a frog which wriggled and tried vainly to get away.

While he held the frog, a turtle crawled awkwardly out of the weeds.

Peter picked up the turtle, too, and again seated himself on the rock.

He held the frog up close, then gave a gasp of surprise. "Why, he's pretty!" exclaimed Peter.

The frog blinked his eye-curtains as if to say, "Of course I am; but how would you know that, you never look!"

The turtle regarded Peter solemnly. Perhaps he was thinking.

"I wonder if all the other things that live in the woods and fields are as exciting to look at," Peter asked himself. He held the frog up closer and then saw something that made him smile. There in the frog's eye he saw . . . himself.

"Do I look that little to you?" Peter asked the frog. "Or do I look like a mountain? I'd like to see things the way you do once."

"Werp!" cried the frog.

"Excuse me," apologized Peter, "I guess I squeezed you a little tight."

In Peter's other hand the turtle made

a brave attempt to get away. He stretched his neck and worked all his feet in the air. But Peter held him firmly by the edge of his shell.

The sun gleamed on the turtle's handsome spots, and on the rich green of the frog's smooth skin. Peter liked their looks.

Then Bob came down through the meadow. "Hi, Pete," he greeted his friend.

"Hello, Bob. Say, look here, will you?" and Peter held up his captives.

"Where did you get 'em?" asked Bob, eagerly.

"Just caught them in the grass. Aren't they pretty?"

"Yes, they're kind of pretty," admitted

Bob. "What I like to do, though, is watch."

"I never did watch them," said Peter.

"Well, let's," Bob suggested.

"Let's what?"

"Let's watch 'em. See where they go and what they do," said Bob.

"All right," agreed Peter. "I never really did look at frogs and turtles, before."

"We'll see a lot of other things, too," said Bob.

"What kinds of things?" Peter wanted to know.

"All kinds. Come on."

"I tell you, Bob," now cried Peter excitedly, "Let's look at 'em the way a frog does . . . up close . . . and then we'll see them as if we had frog's eyes!"

"Say, that's a swell scheme," approved Bob. "We can do it all afternoon."

Peter let the frog and the turtle go. The frog immediately started hopping toward a near-by pond and the turtle crawled slowly after him. Then Peter got down on his hands and knees. So did Bob. And the two boys started to follow the leaping frog and the awkward turtle.

"Hi, Bob," cried Peter, turning aside, "come here. Look at the beetle on this log. He's as big as an elephant."

Bob laughed. "I guess that's the way they look to a frog, all right. This is just like taking a frog's-eye view of the world, isn't it?"

The two boys crawled eagerly through the grass down to the edge of the pond.

"Shh . . .," Peter warned. "We've caught up with him."

"Who?" asked Bob.

"The frog . . . there he is; old Benny Frog, himself."

"How do you know that's his name?" whispered Bob.

"He just looks so important that he ought to be called Benny," Peter replied.

"Wonder what he sees," Bob mused.

"Say, Bob," Peter burst in, "I'll bet he doesn't know that we have decided to be frogs this afternoon, and that anything we see will look just the same to us as it does to him."

"Of course he doesn't," scoffed Bob. "But let's find out what he's looking at."

"Yes, let's," said Peter.

There in the rushes was a mother

Leopard Frog watching over the largest mass of frog's eggs the boys had ever seen in their lives.

"She's counting them," announced Peter.

"No, she isn't. Even a dumb creature like a frog would know that would be a waste of time. She's probably wondering how many of 'em will hatch into tadpoles. Most of the eggs will get eaten anyway. Fish'll eat 'em and snakes, too!"

"How do snakes like 'em, Bob, fried or scrambled?"

"The way they get 'em," laughed Bob.

"Hey," said Peter, "speaking of snakes . . . there are some snake's eggs over there on that rock . . . and look who's right by them."

"Oh, I don't think they are snake's eggs. They look like turtle ones to me," said Bob.

"But, Bob look at the tadpoles with the mother frog!"

"Tadpoles, yes . . . but they ought to be called tad-frogs," laughed Bob. "One of them *is* a frog except for his tail, and the other one is just one step behind him."

"What's over there in the sand . . . no, not there, but over to the right. Come on, Bob," said Peter, "let's hurry over there and see."

There they saw the answer to the question of the eggs.

"Wow! Look at the little turtles hatching!" shouted Bob.

"We're lucky we got here just this minute, when they're crawling out. I'll bet this is something people almost never see," said Peter. He picked up one of the turtles. "Why his shell is all soft!" exclaimed he.

"Sure he's soft. But I'll bet before the day is over he'll get all hard and his shell will protect him," said Bob.

"Of course it will," agreed Peter.

As if to make sure all was well, a large turtle came along just then to watch the hatching party.

"Why, that's our friend the turtle," Bob announced, and Peter nodded his agreement.

The boys lay very still. They were glad they were quiet, for with a loud chattering cry, and a great beating of wings, a Kingfisher alighted for a moment on the turtle's broad back.

"Free ride to the pond," whispered Peter. "Catching fish in his claws must be great fun for a Kingfisher."

"But they don't do that," Bob declared. "They fold their wings and dive head first, and then catch the fish with their bills."

"Well, I never," said Peter.

From the pond came a sound like the one you make when you rub a toy balloon with a dry finger. So they looked.

There was a toad with his throat swelled up.

"Just like mumps," Bob murmured. "I had mumps this winter."

"It isn't mumps, though. Look over there in front of him. See?"

"Oh, yes, — it's another toad."

"It's his mate, I guess. Maybe he is calling her when he makes that noise. Just as if he said: 'You've been swimming long enough. Come on out and sit on the beach a while!'" Peter chuckled.

"You're right, Pete, — look at them coming out — let's follow them for a minute."

"Yes, let's," said Peter.

So they watched the two toads go hop — hop — hopping out of the water and up the bank until they stopped to rest under the shelter of some toadstools.

Peter and Bob waited, but the toads just sat, slowly blinking their eyes with the queer little shutter that closes and opens. Frogs, toads and turtles have shutters like that. They blink them and the eye-curtains protect their eyes like goggles. Snakes have no such eye-lids, and their eyes stay open all the time.

"Well, if they are just going to sit and do nothing, let's go on," said Bob.

"Here's another on a rock," announced Peter. "And he's not alone."

"No, — he's got his cousin with him," laughed Bob.

"What do you know about that!" shouted Bob. "That little toad certainly found a good place for himself."

. "Hey," corrected Peter. "The little one isn't a toad at all — he's a Tree Frog.

Dad showed me one once in the museum. I guess this one dropped out of some of these trees."

"Yes, that's so. And look what queer toes he has — with little suckers on each one," Bob replied.

Peter suggested, "Let's look and see if there are any more Tree Frogs around here."

"They're cute little things," said Bob.

"Yes, there is another one," called Bob, "here on this bare branch."

"I don't see it," said Peter.

"Right here, Pete."

"No wonder I couldn't see him. . . he matches the bark. I guess that's why you almost never see them in trees. I'll bet he's cold and clammy."

"No," said Bob, "my uncle says that cold-blooded things like frogs only are cold if the air is, or if they have been in cold water or mud. If the weather is hot, why, they get hot, too."

Peter touched the Tree Frog. "This one's warm, Bob."

It only wiggled when Peter touched it.

"Well then, he's been in the sun, I guess," said Bob. "But, Peter, up there among the blossoms . . . look!"

"Two of 'em! Golly, aren't they queer looking, Bob?"

Bob shook the branch a little, but the Tree Frogs clung and didn't budge.

"Goodness," said Peter. "Those little suckers on their feet are great to hold on with!"

"Just like that little rubber sucker your Dad has stuck on the windshield of your car to hold cigar ashes," answered Bob.

"But they can move them whenever they want to; they just use one foot at a time and hang on with the other three."

"That's what they do," said Bob.

"Peter . . . the lady toad's gone!" Bob pointed at the spot under the toad-stools.

Peter turned, and sure enough the old man toad was sitting alone, appearing very lonesome and sad.

"Is he sick, do you think, Bob?"

"No, I guess he's just a lazy old lump. He doesn't act as though he had an idea in the world," Bob chuckled. "Uncle Bob knows a lot about toads. He says that's how they get their food. A toad fools flies into thinking he's not interested in them, and then his tongue goes looping out . . . and the flies go down his craw."

"Tough luck for the flies," said Peter.

"Look at him close, Peter! Did you

ever see such a homely, bumpy, lumpy old thing?"

"No. What's he covered with — warts?"

"They look like warts but they aren't. They just help him to look like the dirt he's sitting on, Uncle Bob says — and so no one can see him."

"Wonder what those little flat places are right back of his eyes. Did your uncle say, Bob?"

"Sure, those are his ear drums — he's got them right out like that instead of having ears like ours with the ear drums inside. He doesn't need them protected like ours, I guess."

"Well, I like them our way better," remarked Peter.

"Is he going to eat that spider?" inquired Peter.

"Probably too much like work for him," laughed Bob.

They watched the toad, waiting for his next move, but he didn't make any next move. He just sat there, looking and looking.

The spider went on spinning a delicate web to protect her bag of eggs. By and by the little spiders would hatch and then ——

But Bob and Peter couldn't wait so they crawled off into the woods to see what else they could see.

At the very first tree at the edge of

the wood, Peter touched Bob and said, "Look! What's that — hanging there on the shelf-fungus?"

"What luck!" gloated Bob. "It's a bat taking his daytime nap!"

"He doesn't look like much — hanging up that way like an old coat!" remarked Peter.

"Look how those little hooks on his wings grip the thing, Pete! I guess the reason we haven't been chewed by mosquitoes today is thanks to the bats around here. Mosquitoes are their favorite food, Uncle Bob says. And where there are lots of bats, the long-nosed buzzers just aren't. Three cheers for bats!"

"Make it four!" said Peter.

Soon, the two boys came upon a Cicada sunning himself on an oak branch.

"Peter!" cried Bob. "He's just come out of his shell!"

"Where?" asked Peter.

"There, on the acorn — that's his empty shell. He just humped his back, cracked the shell, and crawled out, leaving the shell behind."

"What do you think he's going to do now, Bob?"

"Just wait for the sun to dry his wings. Then he'll fly off and be a pest, and make farmers mad. That's what Uncle Bob says, anyway."

Peter looked at his friend respectfully. "I'm glad you've listened to your uncle, even though I've never stopped to look at things," he said.

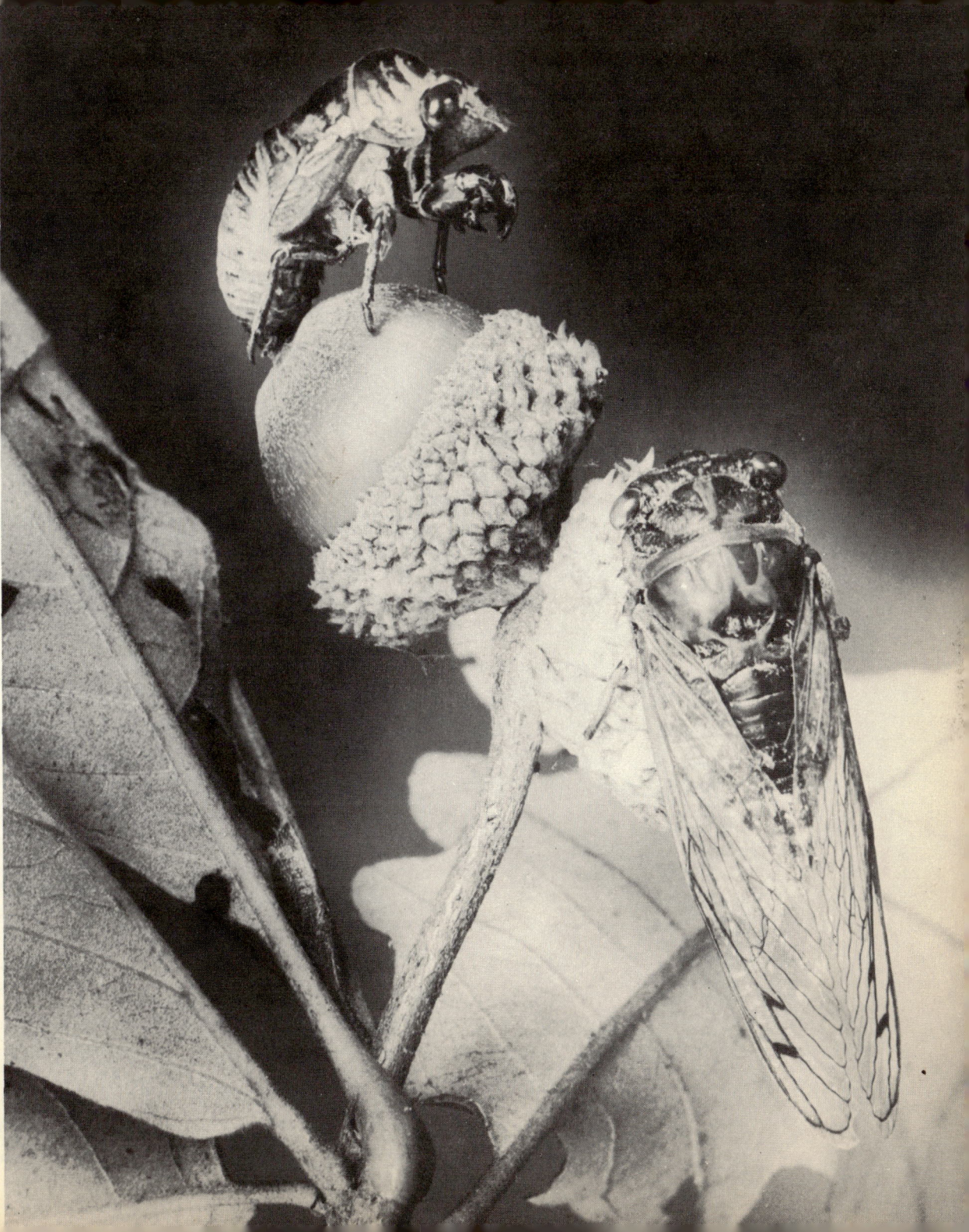

There was a hopping in the grass, so the two boys lay quietly and looked to see what was stirring. Peering through the tall weeds, they saw nearly the strangest sight of the day. For a frog came into a tiny clearing, and on his back rested a beautiful moth.

"The frog looks pleased," whispered Bob.

"Yes, he does. Don't you think it tickles his back when the moth moves its feet?"

"I don't know . . . I never had one walk on my back," laughed Bob.

The moth flew to a branch of a low bush just then, so Peter and Bob crept nearer. Ever so silently they crawled but just as they came within a few inches of the drowsy moth, a twig broke under Peter's knee with a loud snap!

The moth was startled and his feathery antennae flew up, waving nervously, as he tried to find where the danger lay.

"My — they're scary things, moths are," Peter whispered.

"But, say, those things that stuck up are what he hears with," said Bob.

"Just like a radio aerial," announced Peter.

"Let's see what some bugs are doing,

shall we?" suggested Peter as the moth flew away. "We can have some fun if we can find a beetle."

"Beetles are pretty good — they can do things," agreed Bob. "There's one now on that Queen Anne's Lace, and he's talking to a grasshopper."

"Ole grasshopper looks as though he was saying, 'Get off here. I found this place first!'" laughed Peter.

"Maybe he'll squirt tobacco juice in the beetle's eye!" said Bob.

"Maybe," Peter agreed, "But look over there on that log!"

Bob shouted, "This will be a battle!" for a Stag Beetle and a Longhorn Beetle were facing each other and acting as though the log weren't big enough for two!

"You can almost hear them growling!" laughed Peter.

Down went the Longhorn's head and he rushed forward. But the Stag was ready for him and nipped him smartly. Tossing his pinchers, he stood back.

"There goes the long-horned one — he's going around!" said Bob; and sure enough he did move aside and let the Stag Beetle walk down the middle of the log and off into the weeds.

"Let's follow him," suggested Peter.

"Yes, let's," agreed Bob.

"Oh boy! See what he's found now!" cried Bob, pointing.

"It's a little spider," said Peter, leaning forward eagerly, "that'll get all chewed up if he starts anything. He's soft, and the beetle could finish him in one nip. Watch."

"That spider knows a thing or two," said Bob. "Look at him go over that leaf as though that was what he meant to do all along."

" 'Goodbye, Mister Beetle . . . I'm glad I saw you first. I've got a sick grandmother up the street, and this is where I turn off.' I'll bet that is what the spider said," laughed Peter.

"I'll bet," said Bob.

But the beetle didn't seem interested

in the spider at all. He stood still for a moment, looking in exactly the opposite direction. Then he hurried off, with Bob and Peter closely following. In a moment they saw what he was looking for — four other beetles.

"See him now," whispered Bob. "He must be telling his friends something."

"All about what he's been doing this afternoon, I guess," said Peter.

Bob grinned, "Yes. 'Well, fellows,'— that's what he's saying —'you should have seen me just now! I was crossing a log, when thirty or forty great big Long-horn Beetles got around me. They rushed at me and gnashed their pinchers. But I wasn't afraid. What did I do? I bit off their heads; every one of them!' "

Peter laughed, "He's an awful liar. Look, now he's telling them about the spider. 'Hey, you beetles — just before I got here I was coming along minding my own business when a spider four times as big as I am dropped out of a tree onto my back. I fought him for an hour and finally killed him just as his friends arrived to finish me off. I barely escaped with my life!' "

"My, how beetles can lie!" agreed Bob.

"Let's look at the spider a minute," Peter suggested. "Where did it go?"

"Mighty fierce old spider he is too," announced Bob, with a laugh. "Look how dangerous he is."

Peter peered under the leaf that Bob was holding up, and there he saw a fly quietly walking on the spider's broad back.

"I never saw anything like that before!" said Peter. "Why doesn't the spider eat him up?"

"The spider's still thinking about his narrow escape from the beetle, I guess, and anyway he probably isn't hungry."

"That's it. I have watched spiders in our garage. Why even when a spider catches a fly in a web, he doesn't eat him right away. He just spins a web around it and waits till he's good and hungry."

"Lucky for this fly that that's so," said Bob.

"It certainly is," agreed Peter.

Just then a striped insect appeared near the spider.

"Say, here's a fellow a long way from dinner," shouted Peter.

"It's a Potato Bug," said Bob. "He's three miles from the nearest potato patch on Gene Cook's farm. He's got some travelling to do, and I'll bet he's a freak, because I never saw one out of the potato patch."

"It's too bad he's such a pest," said Peter thoughtfully. "He's pretty; so shiny and bright. But he has to be killed."

"I'm glad we decided to look close and see how pretty these little bugs and animals really are."

"Thanks to my idea of having a frog's-eye view!" said Peter.

"Yes . . . thanks to that," said Bob.

"Talking of pretty things, what do you think of these beauties, Peter?" Bob now asked breathlessly.

For on a twig in front of them a lovely Monarch Butterfly was looking intently into the face of a glittering Silverspot.

"Old Silverspot's got his chin in the air, hasn't he, Peter?"

"Yes, and the Monarch is saying 'You aren't half as pretty as I am!' "

"And Silverspot's saying back at him 'Just gaudy and flashy, that's all you are. And besides, you're awfully common. There are millions like you!' "

"My, butterflies talk rough to each other, don't they?" said Bob, grinning.

"Very!" said Peter.

And they winked at each other, there in the woods, before they prowled on.

"I wonder if this butterfly came from a caterpillar like the one on the twig?" asked Bob, stopping near a birch log.

"I don't think so," Peter answered. "Why, they don't seem to like each other at all. Look — the old caterpillar's got his nose down — and the butterfly's got his up, as if to say 'I don't know you!'"

"Joe's got a butterfly like that in his collection," said Bob. "I remember the name of it, too. It's a 'Painted Beauty.' Joe's got it pinned on a cork with its wings all spread out."

"I don't think I'm going to like butterfly collections after today, not-so-much, anyway. Butterflies are much nicer alive and flying around," said Peter.

"Oh, much nicer this way," agreed Bob.

"Dead bugs and stuffed animals aren't

good for anything. What can they do? It's the doing that counts," said Bob.

"Sure, that's what counts. Like that bee there in the blossoms. What bees do is great," remarked Peter.

"A bee gets his nose into more sweet places than any other thing in the woods and meadows. He doesn't waste any time resting and is always looking around for sweets."

"Apple-blossom honey is the sweetest you ever tasted, Bob."

"Well, clover honey is my favorite," Bob announced. "You know what, Pete? I'm going to read up on bees. I'd like to know more about them."

"It would be great to know all about bees and all the other things we are seeing this afternoon," agreed Peter.

"There's lots to know about insects

and animals," agreed Bob. "I've got about a dozen questions for my uncle, right now, about what we've seen today."

"So have I," said Peter. The boys made their way back to the pond again. Resting lightly on a water lily, a Dragon Fly stirred its transparent wings.

"Pete, did you ever notice that a Dragon Fly looks like an airplane?"

"Yes, some," answered Peter, "but I think it's more like an autogyro because it can stop in the air whenever it wants to. It can keep still, then dart and dip around to catch mosquitoes."

Bob pushed aside some branches and motioned to Peter. They both watched the Dragon Fly on the water lily.

"My, he's a big one, and what beautiful wings!" cried Peter.

"And you can see right through them," said Bob.

"Clear through," agreed Peter.

There was a rustle to the left of them where the stony meadow came down to the pond.

"Shh . . . Peter," whispered his friend. "See . . . there by that rock!"

Peter looked and saw the beady eyes and reddish gray body of a nervous little animal.

"It's a woodchuck, isn't it, Bob?"

"Yes. Just a young one, though. He's come out of his house to have a look-see."

"Zip! He saw us. I guess that's his hole there among the rocks. Didn't he go quickly though?" said Peter.

"Like a rocket," Bob agreed. "But woodchucks have more than one entrance to their houses. I'll bet he's watching us from some other doorway right now."

"I'll bet so, too," said Peter.

"What's all that cheeping and twittering there on the ledge?" asked Bob, when they had crawled a little farther.

Peter climbed along the ledge with Bob following him, and there was a nest with four little Phoebes in it.

"They think you're their mother, Pete," laughed Bob. "They're holding their mouths open to you for food."

"I guess they keep their mother busy all right. She has to feed and take care of them all," said Peter.

"All mothers are busy doing that," said Bob. "But I wonder what the father Phoebe does."

"Probably feeds them, too," said Peter.

The boys climbed right down and started to cross the clearing by the pond.

"Look at the old shoe, Bob . . . there in the grass."

"Yes, and I saw it move, too," announced Bob.

"Good reason why . . . see what's coming out of the toe."

Bob whispered, "It's a Deer Mouse, or Whitefooted Mouse. Probably looking around for a good place to live. If she's like the old woman who lived in a shoe, she'll pick a better place to raise her family. Deer Mouse climbers are just like little squirrels."

"There she goes. Let's follow and see what she does."

"Yes . . . let's," said Bob.

"Hey . . . I don't think she's picked a very good place to explore," gasped Peter, for he saw where the Deer Mouse was going next.

"Golly, no!" agreed Bob.

"If the hornets are home in that nest, there'll be a pretty unhappy Deer Mouse around here in a minute or so."

"I feel sorry for her. But we'll soon know if the hornets are in, or if they are out calling on their neighbors, or just horneting around," said Bob.

"Oh . . . she's gone in. I pity her," said Peter.

"So do I," said Bob.

It wasn't long before the mouse came

tumbling out. Not a hornet followed her. Bob was relieved.

"Look at her, Pete!"

"I guess she knew all the time that the hornets weren't there. Don't you think she can hear them or smell them or something?" asked Peter.

"Well, anyway, she isn't going to stay and use that place for a home. Look at her running over those cat-tails in the hollow."

"Come on — let's follow her," said Peter.

"I'm coming," said Bob.

"That old cat-tail, all gone to seed, would make a nice lining for a nest, wouldn't it?" Peter suggested.

"Yes, and she likes it, too. Maybe she's going to take some to line her home with and make a soft bed for her babies," said Bob.

"I think she's just up there to take a look around. It's a keen lookout, Bob."

"Here she comes down, Pete. She acts as if she's seen enough for one day."

"So have we . . . almost," said Peter.

The two boys stood very still as they watched the little Deer Mouse come

down from the cat-tail and go over to a birch tree, which she climbed.

"Look! That's where she lives. See that little hole — that's the door," announced Peter.

"And now she's sitting on her front porch — like Dad when he's come home from work and is waiting for supper."

They waited to see whether the Deer Mouse would go into the hole. But she didn't — because it was a Downy Wood-pecker's home, anyway. Her curiosity had taken her there. Now she just sat as though she were thinking of something. Soon Peter, too, had a thought.

"Say, Bob, it's beginning to get dark. We'd better hustle and go home. Anyway my knees are wrecked."

"So are mine," said Bob. "Yes, we'd better hurry. We've seen things today that we never saw before!"

"We certainly have," said Peter. "We'll

be seeing more from now on, won't we?"

"You bet!" said Bob.

Back in the meadow by the rock they found the frog again. Bob and Peter got down on the ground close to him and Peter said:

"We enjoyed our frog's-eye view today. I guess you knew we would, didn't you?"

But the frog didn't answer, as he solemnly blinked his eyes. Then his wide mouth seemed to smile, as though he were thinking, "Of course. You have good eyes, too."

In fact, Peter and Bob were sure he was going to say those very words, for he opened his mouth.

Then — "Ker-chunk!" and away he hopped.

Peter looked at Bob and Bob looked at Peter.

"I think so, too," said Peter.

"And so do I," said Bob.

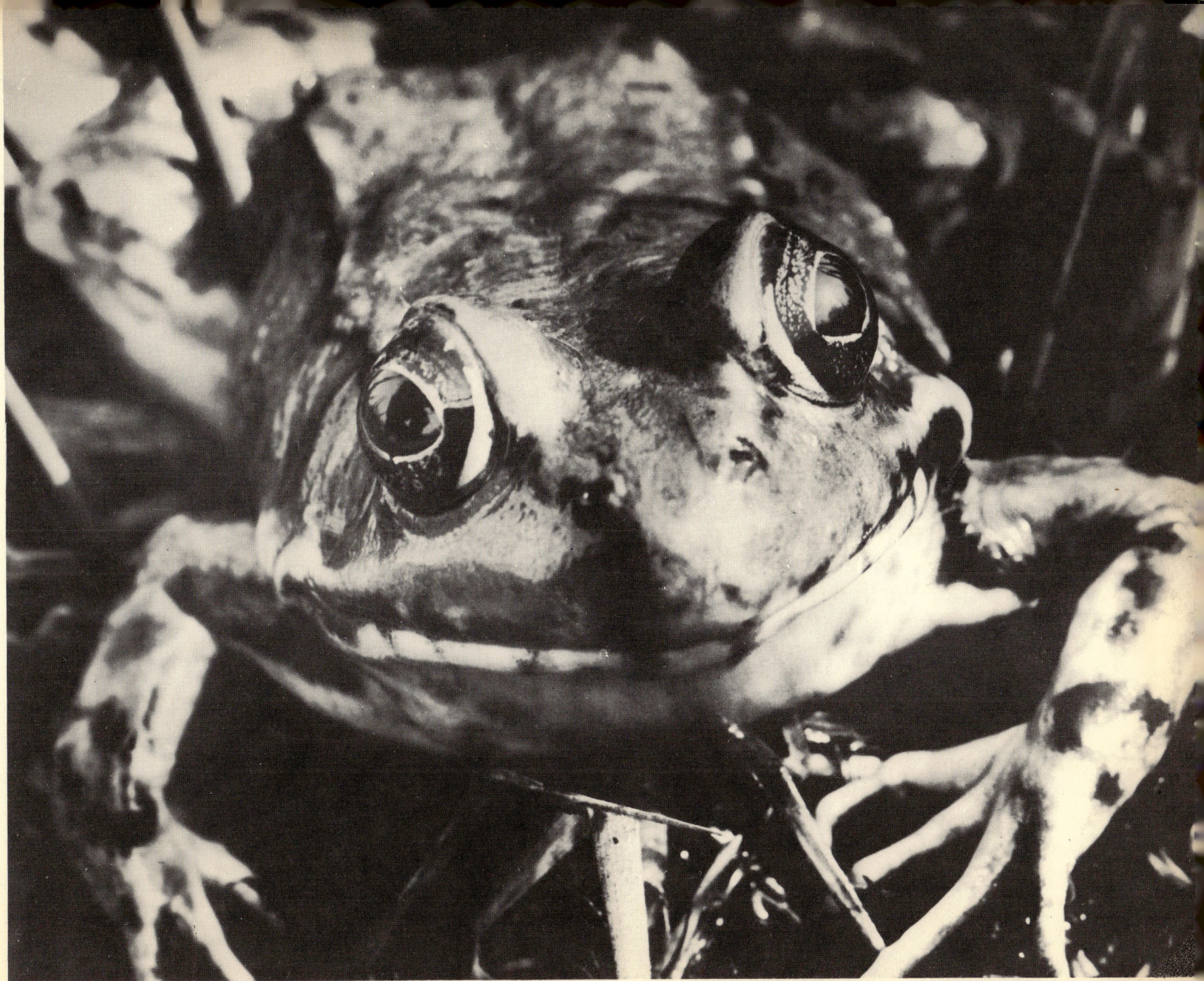